THE BEST OF
IRON MAIDEN

Exclusive distributors:
Music Sales Limited, 8/9 Frith Street, London W1V 5TZ, England.
Music Sales Pty Limited, 120 Rothschild Avenue, Rosebery, NSW 2018, Australia.

This book © Copyright 1991 by Wise Publications.
Order No. AM84054 ISBN 0.7119.2577.1

Compiled by Peter Evans. Typset by Capital Setters.

Music Sales' complete catalogue lists thousands of titles and is free from your local music shop, or direct from Music Sales Limited.
Please send a cheque/postal order for £1.50 for postage to: Music Sales Limited, Newmarket Road, Bury St. Edmunds, Suffolk IP33 3YB.

Your Guarantee of Quality:
As publishers, we strive to produce every book to the highest commercial standards.
The book has been carefully designed to minimise awkward page turns and to make playing from it a real pleasure.
Particular care has been given to specifying acid-free, neutral-sized paper which has not been chlorine bleached but produced with special regard for the environment.
Throughout, the printing and binding have been planned to ensure a sturdy, attractive publication which should give years of enjoyment.
If your copy fails to meet our high standards, please inform us and we will gladly replace it.

Printed in Great Britain by Redwood Books, Trowbridge, Wiltshire

WISE PUBLICATIONS
LONDON / NEW YORK / SYDNEY

Tablature and Instructions Explained

OPEN C CHORD

SCALE OF E MAJOR

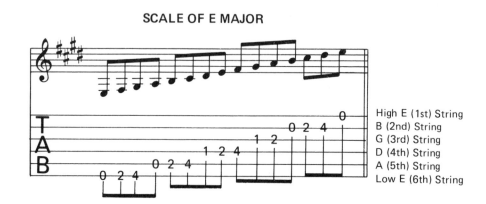

High E (1st) String
B (2nd) String
G (3rd) String
D (4th) String
A (5th) String
Low E (6th) String

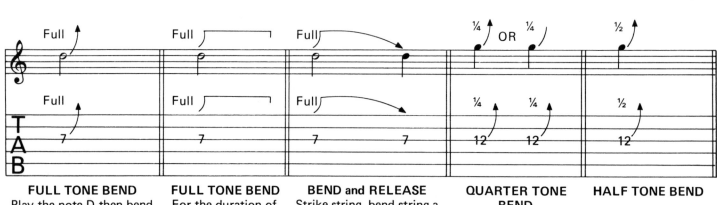

FULL TONE BEND
Play the note D then bend the string so that the pitch rises by one tone to E.

FULL TONE BEND
For the duration of symbol line.

BEND and RELEASE
Strike string, bend string a full tone then release bend while string is still sounding, as indicated.

QUARTER TONE BEND

HALF TONE BEND

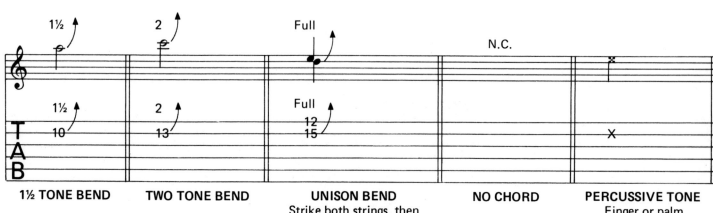

1½ TONE BEND

TWO TONE BEND

UNISON BEND
Strike both strings, then bend the lower string up to the pitch of the higher one.

NO CHORD

PERCUSSIVE TONE
Finger or palm mute on strings.

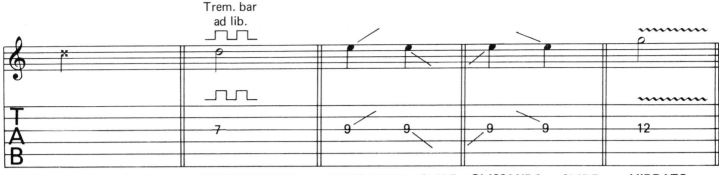

This symbol seen in the vocal line means that the lyrics were either spoken or shouted rhythmically in an approximation of the pitches shown.

TREMOLO BAR VIBRATO EFFECT

GLISSANDO or SLIDE Up or down from a note.

GLISSANDO or SLIDE Up or down to a note.

VIBRATO

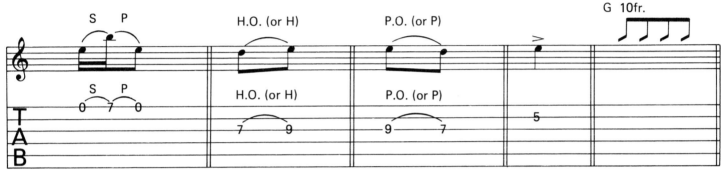

In the passages where 'S' instruction appears over a note, (as in the above example) hit the string over the given fret (as indicated in tablature) with the edge of your plectrum. Whenever the 'P' instruction appears after an 'S', simply remove the plectrum from the string, in the manner of a 'Pull Off'.

HAMMER ON Hammer a finger down on the next note without striking the string again.

PULL OFF Pull your finger off the string with a plucking motion to sound the next note without stiking the string again with your plectrum.

STRESS MARK

RHYTHM SLASHES In the above example play the G chord at the 10th fret in the timing shown by the slashes.

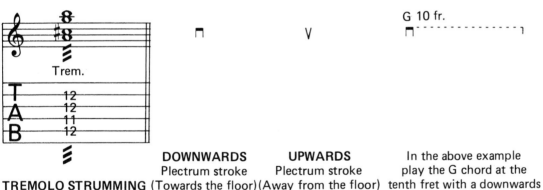

TREMOLO STRUMMING Fast up and down stroke strumming.

DOWNWARDS Plectrum stroke (Towards the floor)

UPWARDS Plectrum stroke (Away from the floor)

In the above example play the G chord at the tenth fret with a downwards plectrum stroke, then let the chord sound for the duration of the dotted line.

Repeat the preceding bar.

Repeat the preceding two bars.

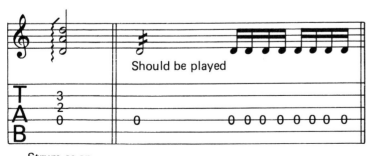

Strum as an arpeggio.

Where there is an instruction saying 'Riff 1' or 'Riff 2', Guitar lick 1 or 2, Guitar Strum 1 or 2 etc . . . take special note of its whereabouts (because later on in the piece you will see 'Riff 1 repeated' or 'Riff 2 repeated', etc.) so you can quickly refer back to the original for the music and tablature.

RUNNING FREE
WORDS & MUSIC BY STEVE HARRIS & PAUL DI'ANNO

Guitar Strum: A

1. Just six - teen, a pick - up truck___
2nd verse
3rd verse

out of mon - ey, out of luck.___ I've got no - where to

call my own.___ Hit the gas,___ and___ here I go.___

I'm run - ning free_____ yeah,___

I'm run - ning free.___

I'm run - ning free_____ yeah,___

To Coda | 1.

oh I'm run - ning free.___ 2. I

5

2.
Guitar Strum: A
C8fr. D10fr. E G 3fr. E
C D E G 3fr. E
C D E C D
2 times
E G7fr. D-I 7fr. D-II G-I
B
"muffled" effect
release "muffled" effect
E C3fr. D5fr.
B
G3fr. E12fr. D10fr. E12fr. D10fr. E12fr. C8fr. D10fr.
I'm run- ning free yeah, I'm run - ning free.
E G3fr. E12fr. D10fr. E12fr. D E 10fr. 12 fr. C8fr. D10fr.
I'm run - ning free yeah, oh I'm run - ning free. Break.
E O.C. E O.C. E C8fr. D10fr.
(Lay left hand across strings for "percussive" strums)

2. Spent the night in an L.A. jail
   And listened to the sirens wail
   They ain't got a thing on me
   I'm running wild, I'm running free.

   Chorus
3. Pulled her at the Bottle Top
   Whiskey, dancing, disco hop
   Now all the boys are after me
   And that's the way it's gonna be.

   Chorus

SANCTUARY

WORDS & MUSIC BY STEVE HARRIS, PAUL DI'ANNO, DAVE MURRAY, CLIVE BURR & DENNIS STRATON

1. Out of the win-ter came a war horse of steel. I've nev-er killed a wo-man be-fore, but I know how it feels. I know you'd have gone in-sane if you saw what I saw so now I've got to look for

(to 2nd end on D.S.)

Lyrics (under the music staves):

I know you'd have gone in - sane if you saw what I saw

so now I've got to look for

sanc - tu - ar - y from the law.

Guitar Lick: A
Dno 3rd

Guitar Lick: B
Dno 3rd

D.S. al Coda

3. So you

Coda

Guitar Lick: B
Dno 3rd

2. I met up with a 'slinger last night to keep me alive.
He spends all his money on gambling and guns to survive.

3. I can laugh at the wind, I can howl at the rain.
Down in the Canyon or out in the plain.

WOMEN IN UNIFORM

WORDS & MUSIC BY GREGORY MacAINSH

Bee - hive hair - do, for - ty - five on the hip, Pa - trol - wo - man San - ders, don't you give her no lip.

Took me to the sta - tion for a breath test, and back to her bed - room for some house ar - rest.

Wo - men___ in u - ni - form,___ some - times they look so cold.___

Wo - men___ in u - ni - form.___ Wo - men___ in u - ni - form,__ but ooh!__ they feel so warm.___

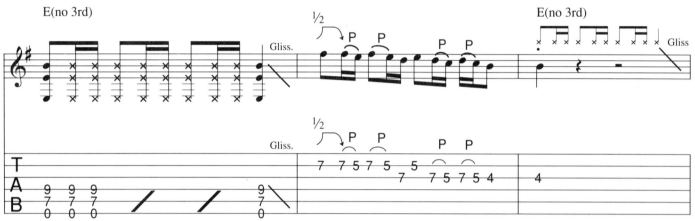

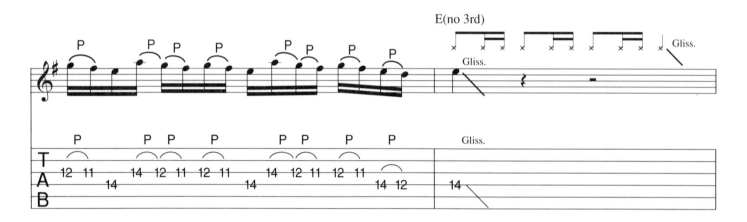

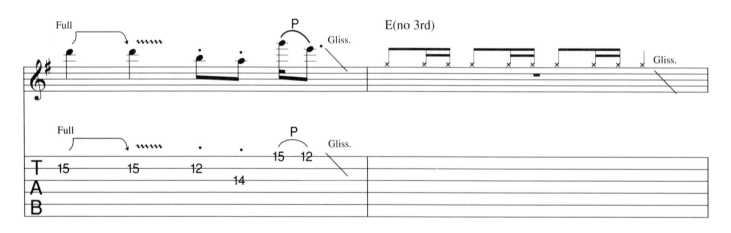

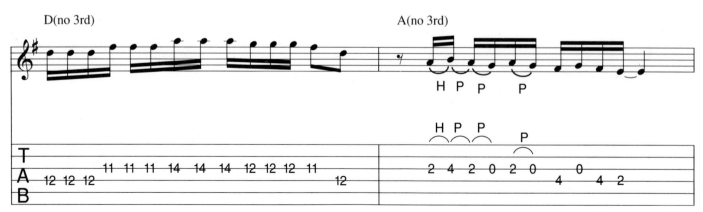

TWILIGHT ZONE

WORDS & MUSIC BY DAVE MURRAY & STEVE HARRIS

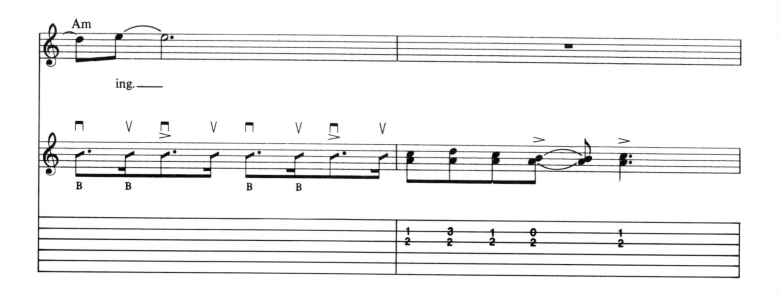

Guitar Lick: B

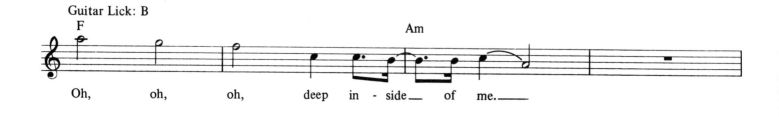

Oh, oh, oh, deep in - side of me.

Oh, oh, oh, can't you see me?

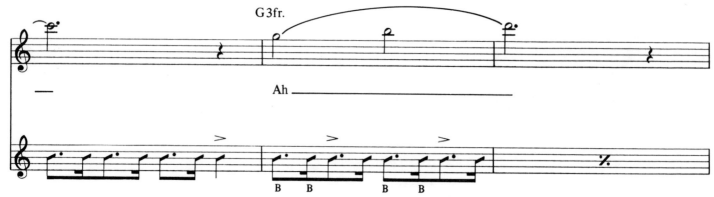

Ah

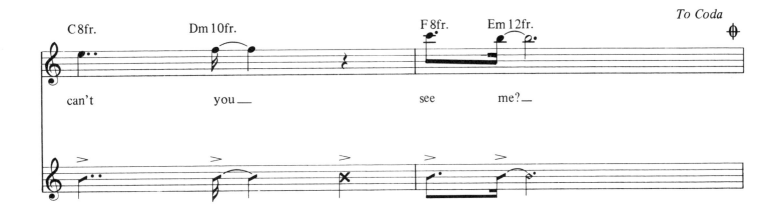

can't   you —   see   me? —

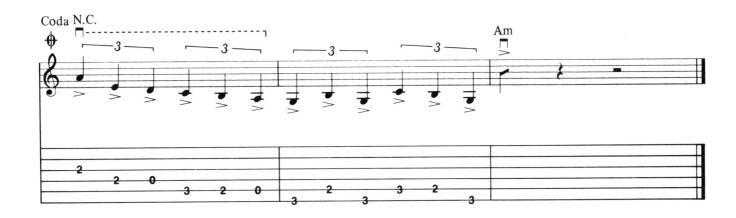

2. I'm looking foreward to her spirit coming over to me.
I feel tempted to bring her over to see just what it's
like to be hanging on the other side.
I feel so lonely, it's a long time since
I died.
I try to show her that she's never gonna be
alone, because my spirit is imprisoned
in the twilight zone.

WRATHCHILD

WORDS & MUSIC BY STEVE HARRIS

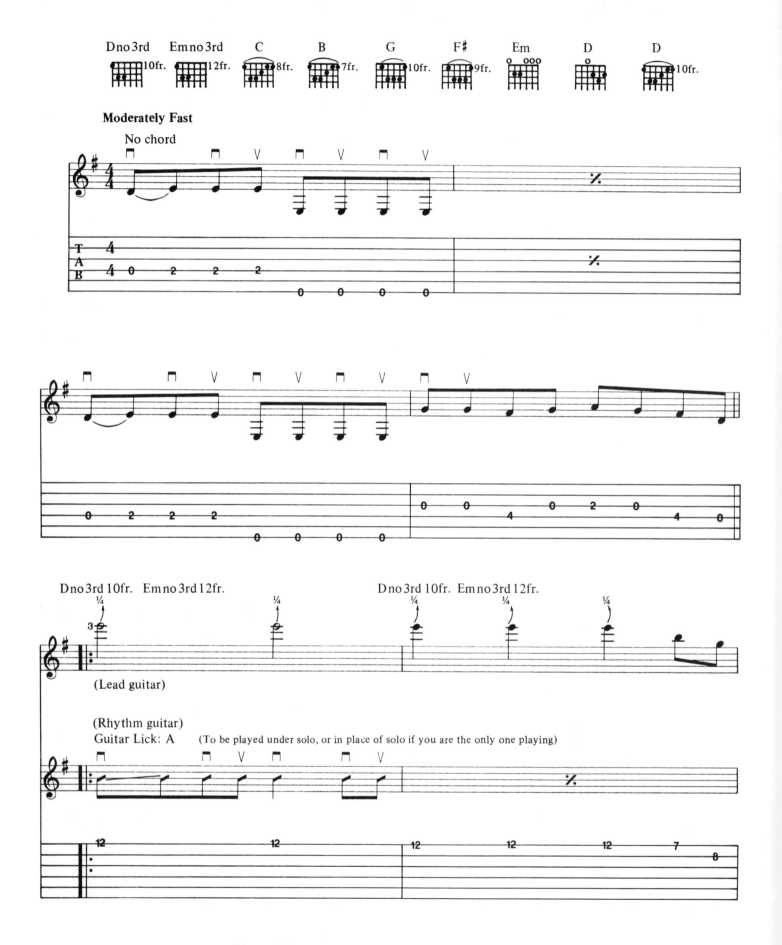

D no 3rd 10fr.   Em no 3rd 12fr.   G 10fr.

Guitar Lick: A continues for rhythm guitar.

D no 3rd 10fr.   Em no 3rd 12fr.   D no 3rd 10fr.   Em no 3rd 12fr.

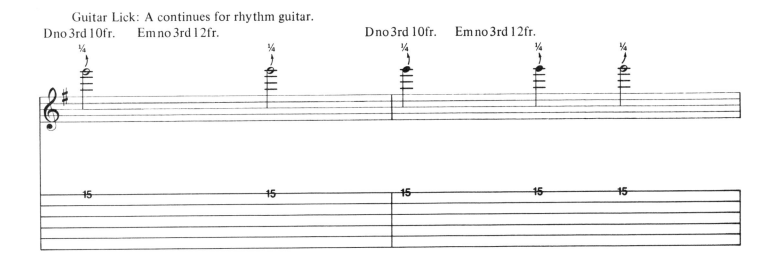

D no 3rd 10fr. Em no 3rd 12fr.   G 10fr.

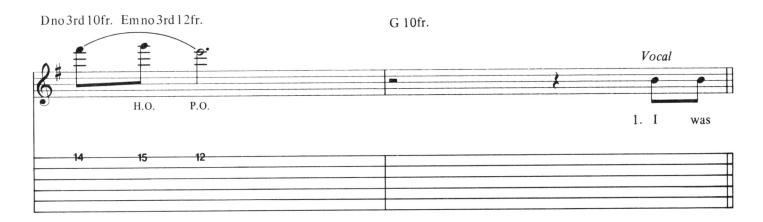

2. Say it doesn't matter
   ain't nothin' gonna alter the
   course of my destination.
   I know I've got to find
   some serious piece of mind,
   or I know I'll just go crazy.

Run to the Hills

WORDS & MUSIC BY STEVE HARRIS

Moderately, but strong and cutting

Guitar Lick: A

Make each bend and shake strong and emphatic

Guitar Lick: A

White man came across the sea He brought us pain and
fought him hard we fought him well Out on the plains we

mis-e-ry he killed our tribes he killed our creed He
gave him hell but man-y came too much for the 'cree' Oh

1.

took our game for his own need We

2. G3fr. D10fr.

will we ev-er be set free.

Faster

Rid - ing thru' dust clouds and bar - ren wastes_
Sol - dier blue in the bar - ren wastes_

gal - lop-ing hard on the plains_
hun - ting and kill - ing their game_

chas - ing the red - skins
rap - ing the wo - men and

back to their holes_
wast - ing the men_

fight - ing them at their own game_
the on - ly good in - dians are tame_

Mur -
Sell -

der for free - dom the stab in the back
ing them whisk - ey and tak - ing their gold

Wo - men and child - ren the
En - slav - ing the young and de -

cow - ards at - tack.
stroy - ing the old.

Chorus

Run to the hills

Run for_ your lives_

Run to the hills

To Coda

Run for your lives. _____

run for your lives.

PURGATORY

WORDS & MUSIC BY STEVE HARRIS

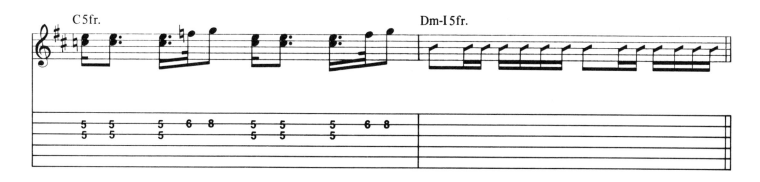

(Play three times)

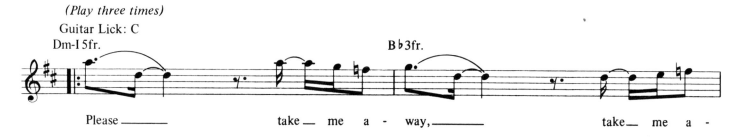

Please _____ take _ me a - way, _____ take _ me a -

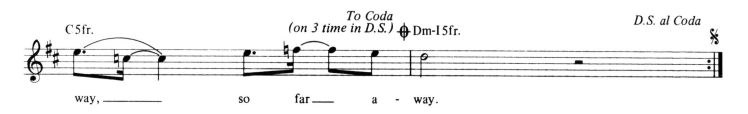

way, _____ so far _ a - way.

way.

(Strum ⊓ & ∨ as fast as you can)

THE NUMBER OF THE BEAST

WORDS & MUSIC BY STEVE HARRIS

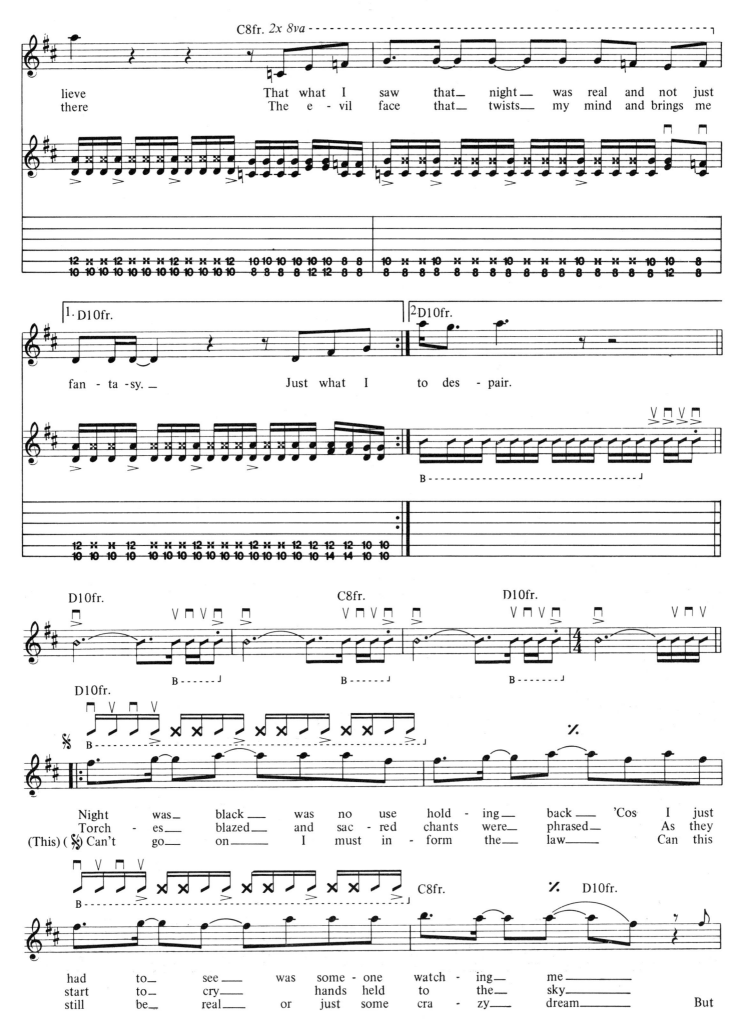

lieve
there

That what I saw that_ night_ was real and not just
The e - vil face that_ twists_ my mind and brings me

fan - ta -sy. _

Just what I to des - pair.

Night was_ black_ was no use hold - ing_ back_ 'Cos I just
Torch - es_ blazed_ and sac - red chants were_ phrased_ As they
(This) Can't go on_ I must in - form the_ law_ Can this

had to_ see _ was some - one watch - ing_ me_
start to_ cry _ hands held to the_ sky_
still be_ real _ or just some cra - zy_ dream_ But

33

In the_ mist_ dark fig-ures move and_ twist was all
In the_ night_ the fires are burn - ing_ bright the ritual
I feel_ drawn_ to - wards the chant - ing_ hordes seems to

this for_ real_ or just some kind of hell_
has be - gun_ or sa - tan's work is done_
mes - mer - ize_ can't a - void their eyes_

Six six six the num - ber of the beast_
Six six six the num - ber of the beast_
Six six six the num - ber of the beast_

Hell and fire_ was born_ to be re - leased._
Sac - ri - fice_ is go - ing on to - night.
Six six six_ the one_

(Repeat 3 times)

turn
force

And I'll pos - sess your bo - dy and I'll make you
I have the power to make my e - vil take it's

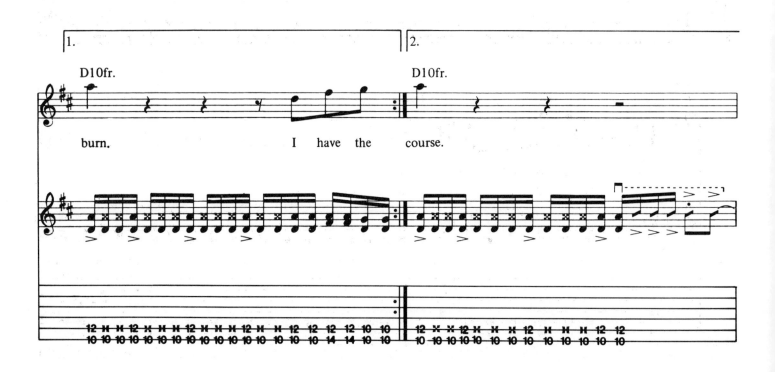

burn.
I have the course.

FLIGHT OF ICARUS

WORDS & MUSIC BY ADRIAN SMITH & BRUCE DICKINSON

THE TROOPER

WORDS & MUSIC BY STEVE HARRIS

1. You take my life but I'll take yours too.___ You'll fire your mus-ket, but I'll

run you through.___ So when you're wait-ing for the

next at-tack, you'd bet-ter stand, there's no turn-ing back.___

The bu-gle sounds, the charge___ be-gins.___

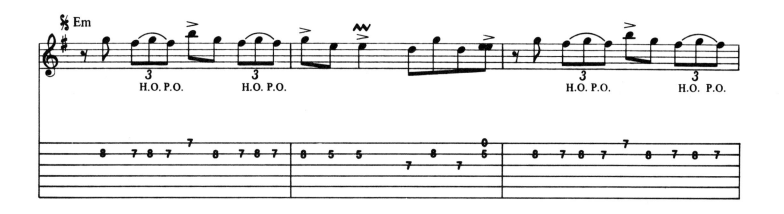

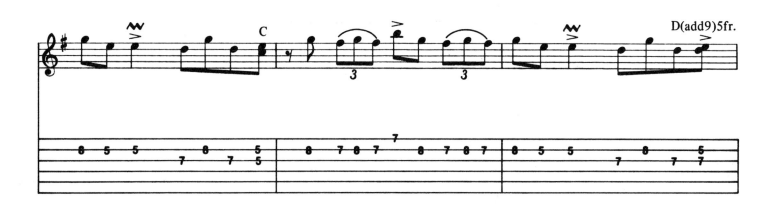

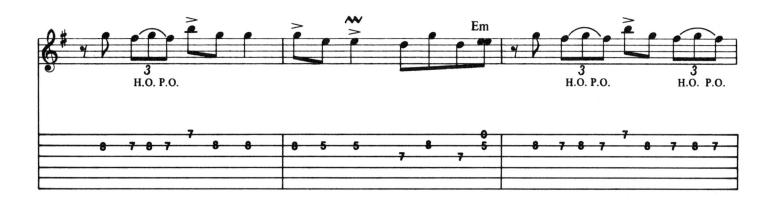

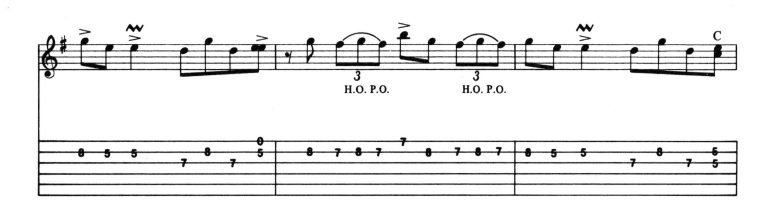

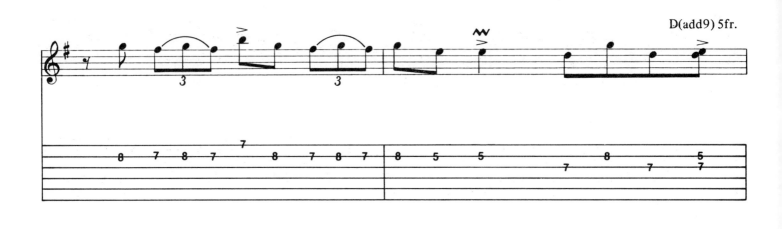

D(add9) 5fr.

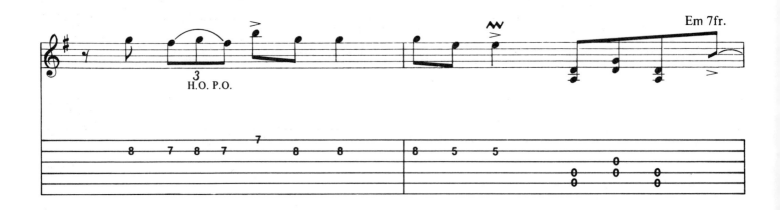

Em 7fr.

H.O. P.O.

Guitar Strum - I

D G D Em 7fr.

2. The horse, he sweats with fear, we break and run.
3. See last page

D G D C 8fr.

The might - y roar of the Rus - sian guns____

D G D Em 7fr.

and as we race to - wards the hu - man wall,

D G D Em 7fr.

the screams of pain as my com - rades fall. __

We hur - dle bo - dies that lay on the ground.

And the Rus - sians fire an - o - ther round.____

We get so near yet so____ far a - way.____

We won't live____ to fight an - o - ther day.

Oh____

Chorus: Strum same as in previous chorus

Oh ____

To Coda

3rd verse: We get so close, near enough to fight
when a Russian gets me in his sights
he pulls the trigger and I feel the blow
A burst of rounds takes my horse below.
And as I lay there gazing at the sky,
my body's numb and my throat is dry.
And as I lay forgotten and alone,
without a tear I draw my parting groan.

2 MINUTES TO MIDNIGHT

WORDS & MUSIC BY STEVE HARRIS

1. Kill for gain or shoot to maim But we don't need a rea-son The

2,3. *See block lyric*

Gold-en Goose is on the loose And nev-er out of sea-son. Some

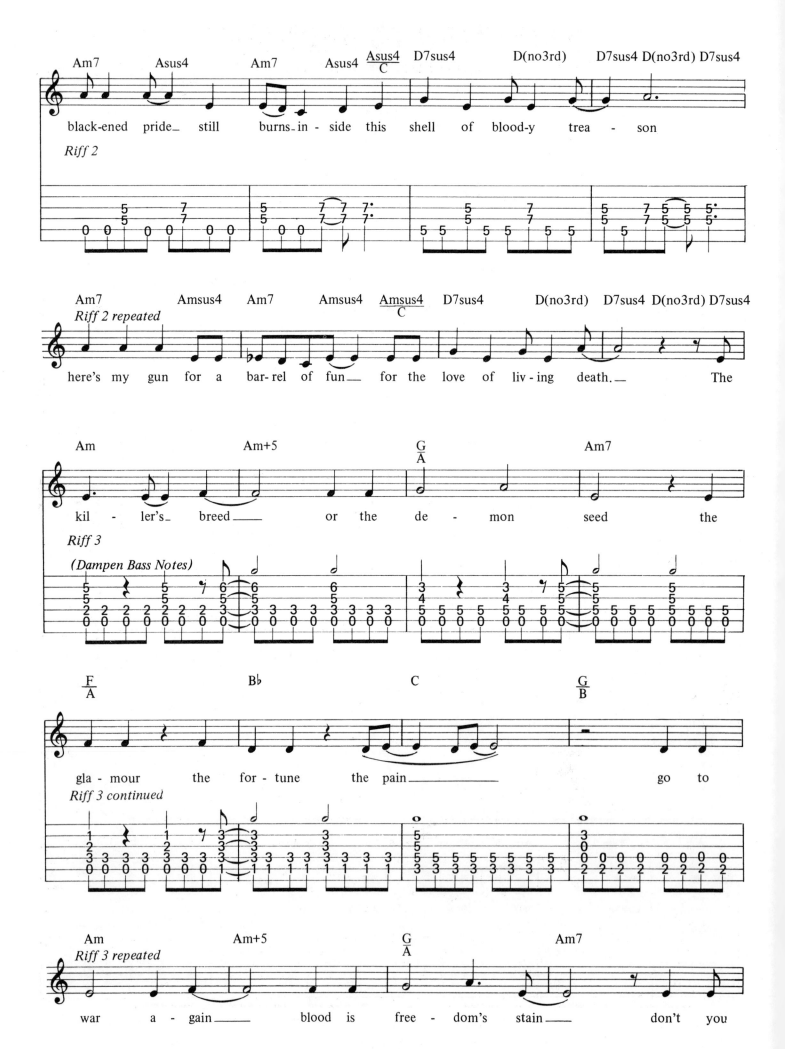

CODA

Verse 2   The blind men shout let the creatures out
We'll show the unbelievers,
The Napalm screams of human flames
Of a prime time Belsen Feast. . . . YEAH!
As the reasons for the carnage cut their meat and lick the gravy,
We oil the jaws of the war machine and feed it with our babies.

Verse 3   The body bags and little rags of children torn in two,
And the jellied brains of those who remain to put the finger right on you,
As the Madmen play on words and make us all dance to their song,
To the tune of starving millions to make a better kind of gun.

ACES HIGH
WORDS & MUSIC BY STEVE HARRIS

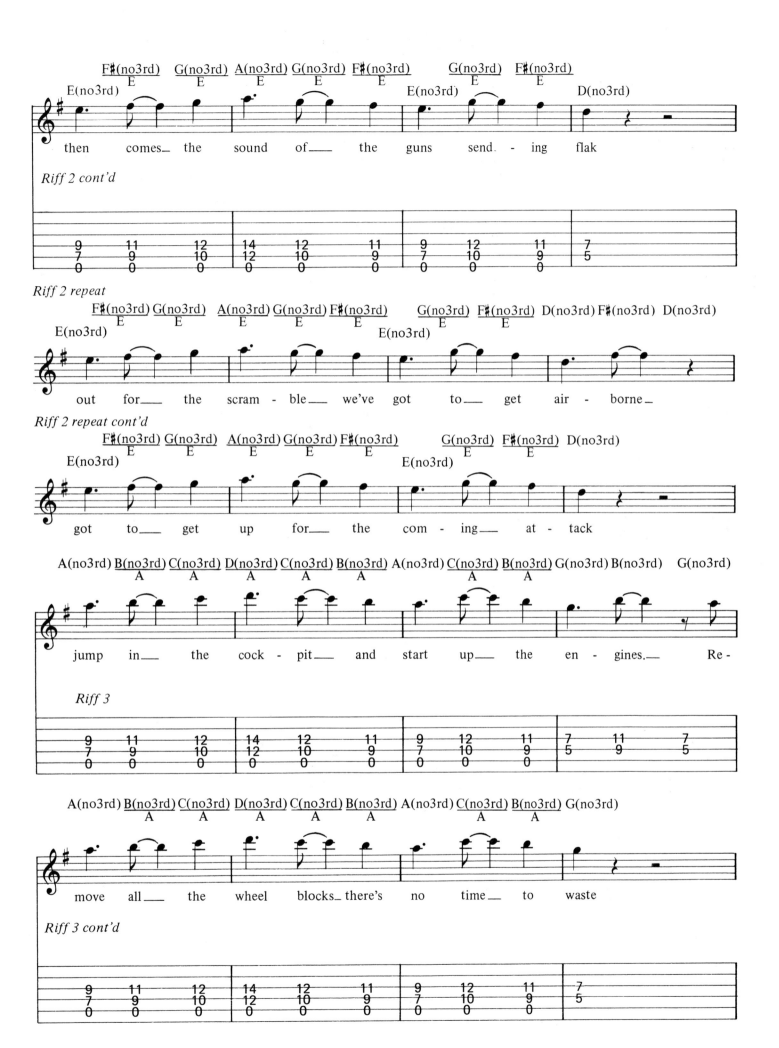

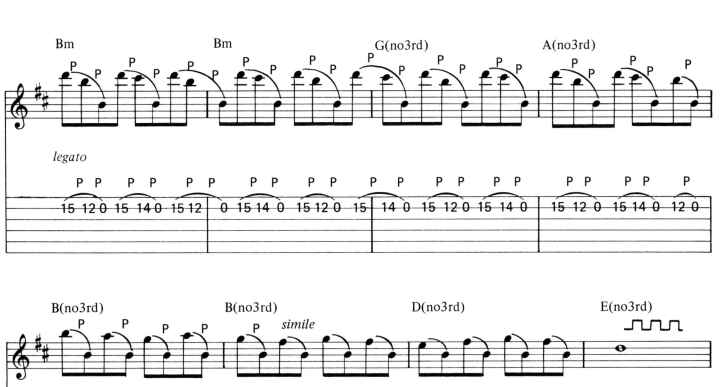

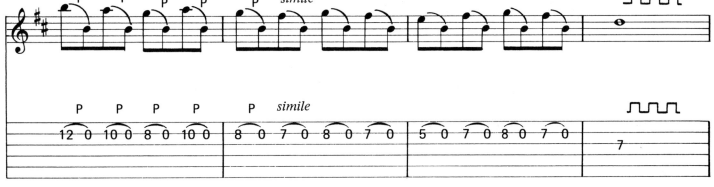

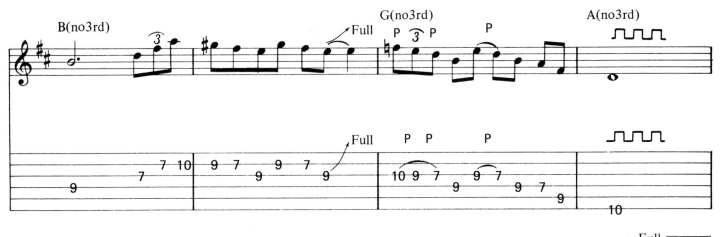

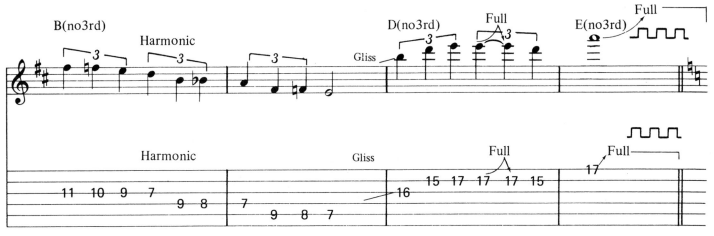

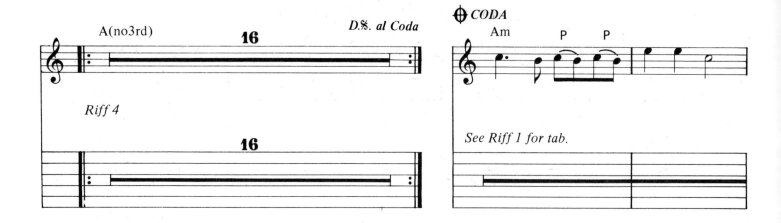

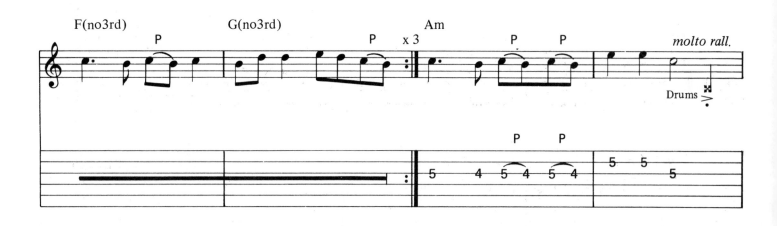

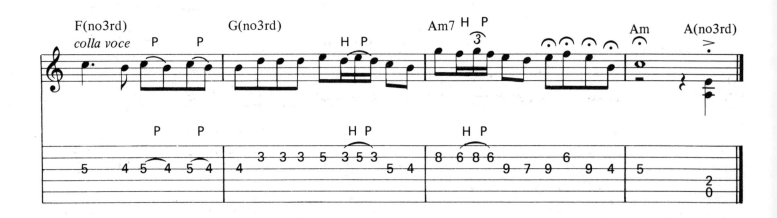

Verse 3   Move in to fire at the mainstream of bombers
Let off a sharp burst and then turn away
Roll over spin round and come in behind them
Move to their blind sides and firing again

Verse 4   Bandits at 8 o'clock move in behind us
Ten ME-109's out of the sun
Ascending and turning our Spitfires to face them
Heading straight for them I press down my guns.

WASTED YEARS

WORDS & MUSIC BY ADRIAN SMITH

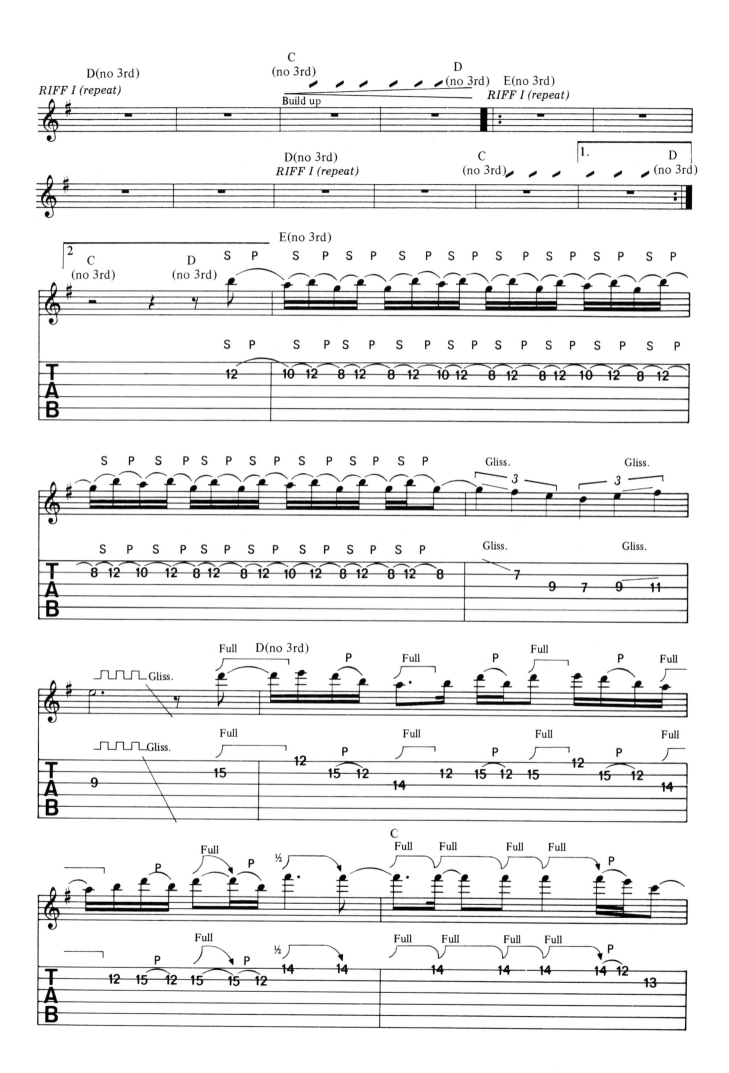

VERSE 3:
Too much time on my hands, I got you on my mind
Can't ease this pain, so easily
When you can't find the words to say it's hard to make it through another day
And it makes me wanna cry and throw my hands up to the sky.

STRANGER IN A STRANGE LAND

WORDS & MUSIC BY ADRIAN SMITH

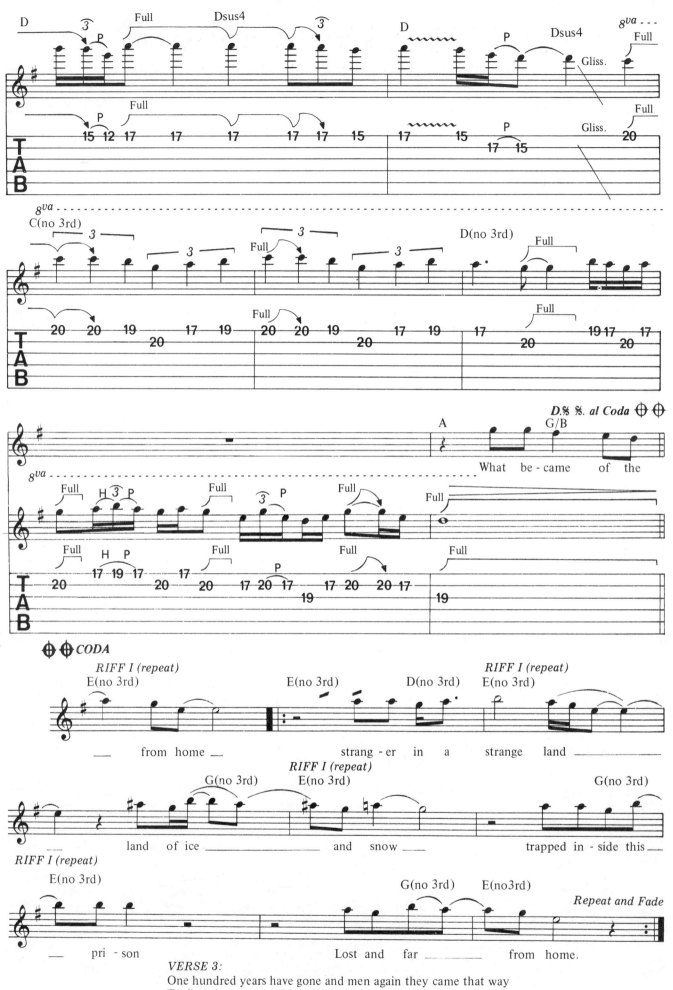

VERSE 3:
One hundred years have gone and men again they came that way
To find the answer to the mystery
They found this body lying where it fell on that day
Preserved in time for all to see
No brave new world, no brave new world
Lost in this place and leave no trace.

CAN I PLAY WITH MADNESS?

WORDS & MUSIC BY ADRIAN SMITH, STEVE HARRIS & BRUCE DICKINSON

VERSE 2:
I screamed aloud to the old man
I said don't lie, don't say you don't know
I say you'll pay for your mischief
In this world or the next
Oh and then he fixed me with a freezing glance
And the hell fires raged in his eyes
He said do you want to know the truth son —
I'll tell you the truth
Your soul's gonna burn in the lake of fire.

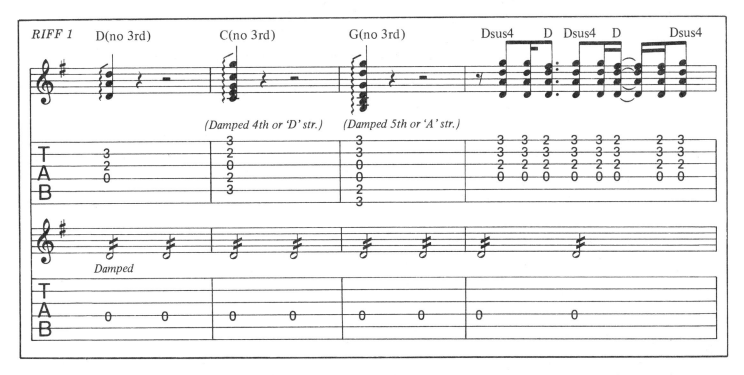

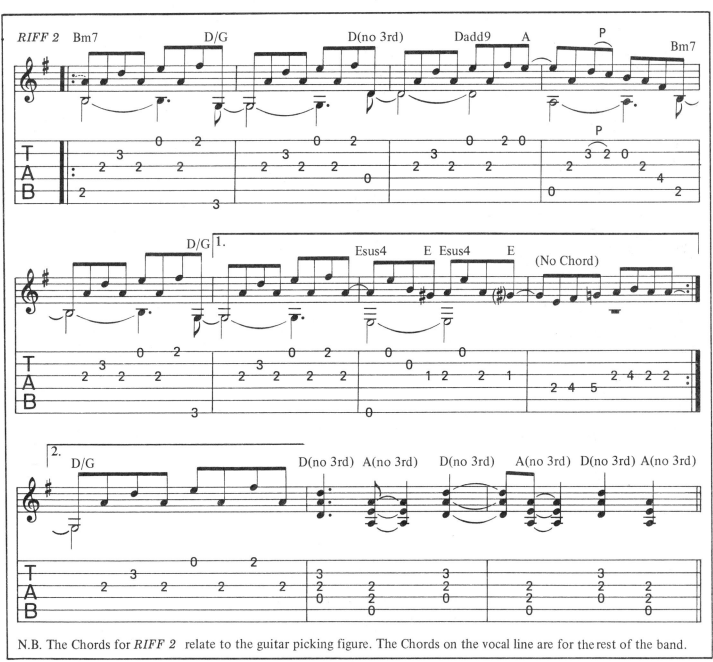

N.B. The Chords for *RIFF 2* relate to the guitar picking figure. The Chords on the vocal line are for the rest of the band.

THE EVIL THAT MEN DO

WORDS & MUSIC BY ADRIAN SMITH, STEVE HARRIS & BRUCE DICKINSON

*The top 'e' and 'b' of the Chord are doubled on the open strings (see tablature).

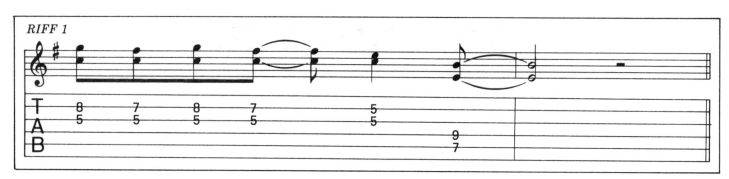

THE CLAIRVOYANT

WORDS & MUSIC BY STEVE HARRIS

*N.B. These triplets have been written 'a tempo' for ease of reading.

†N.B. If you have played the triplet passage at slightly slower than 'a tempo', you will find yourself already some beats into this bar at the time of playing the last 'e' note.

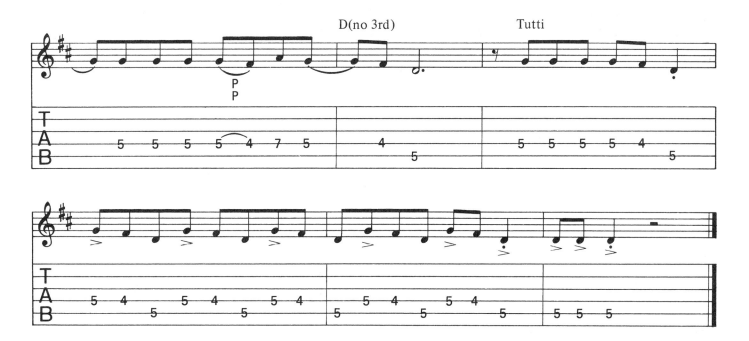

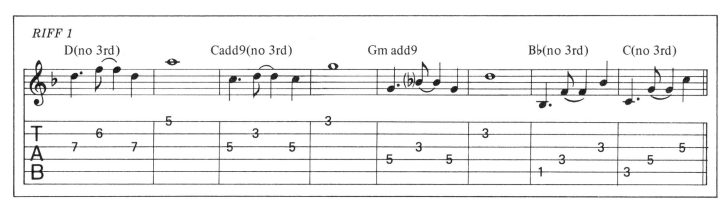

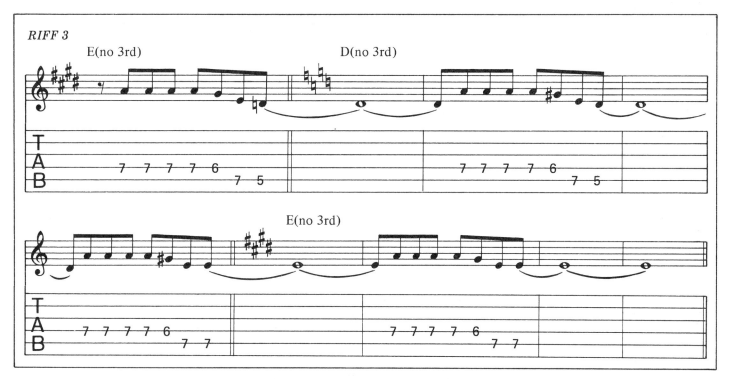

VERSE 3:
Just by looking through your eyes
He could see the future penetrating right in through your mind
See the truth and see your lies
But for all his power couldn't forsee his own demise.

INFINITE DREAMS

WORDS & MUSIC BY STEVE HARRIS

I could-n't hear __ those screams __ e - ven in my wild - est dreams. __

Suf-fo - ca - tion wak - ing in a sweat scared to fall a -

sleep a - gain __ in case the dream be - gins __ a - gain.

Some - one chas - ing I can - not move, __

stand - ing ri - gid a night - mare sta - tue. What a dream __ where

will it end __ and will I tran - scend. _____ Rest - less sleep the

mind in tur - moil one night - mare ends a - no - ther fer - tile.

It's get-ting to me, __ so scared to sleep __ but scared to wake now __

in too __ deep. __ E - ven though it's reached new heights I ra - ther like __ the rest-less nights. It

makes me won - der, makes me think __ there's more to this. __ I'm on the brink, __ it's

not the fear __ of what's be - yond __ it's just that I __ might not re - spond. I

have an in - t'rest al - most cra - ving but would I like to get too far __ in. It

94

BRING YOUR DAUGHTER...TO THE SLAUGHTER

WORDS & MUSIC BY BRUCE DICKINSON

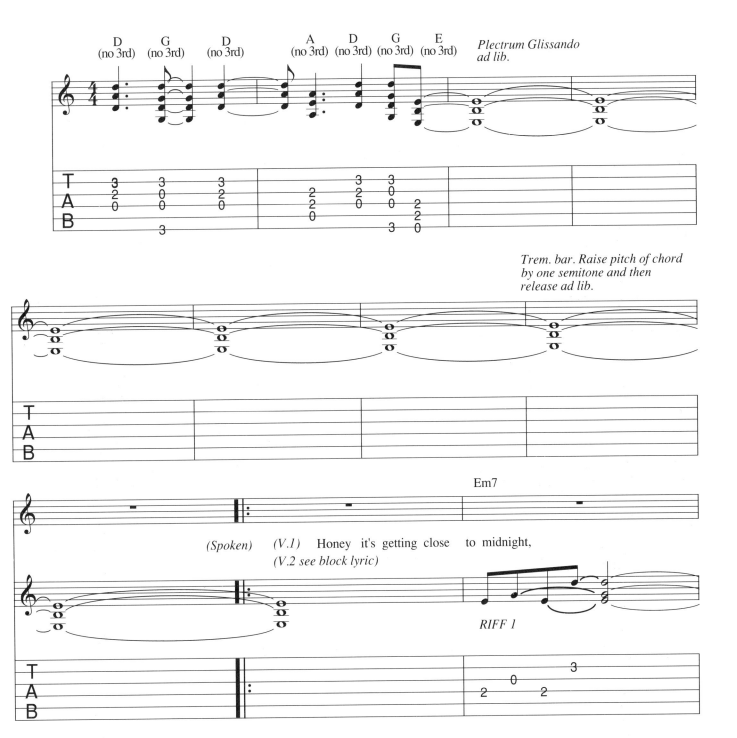

Verse 2:

Honey it's getting close to daybreak,
The sun is creeping in the sky.
No patent remedies for heartache,
Just empty words and humble pie
So get down on your knees honey,
Assume an attitude.
You just pray that I'll be waiting,
'Cos you know I'm coming soon.

HOLY SMOKE

WORDS & MUSIC BY STEVE HARRIS & BRUCE DICKINSON

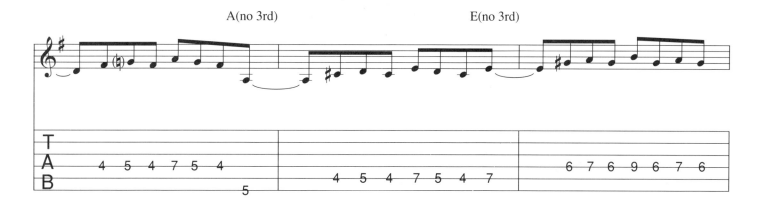

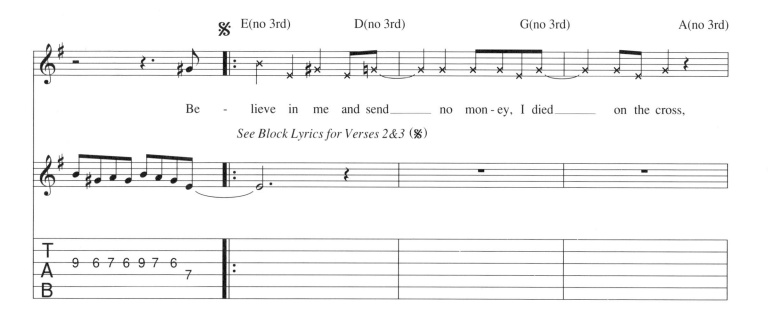

Be - lieve in me and send ____ no mon - ey, I died ____ on the cross,

See Block Lyrics for Verses 2&3 (%)

that ain't fun - ny, but my so called friends, ___ they're mak - ing me a joke, they missed out

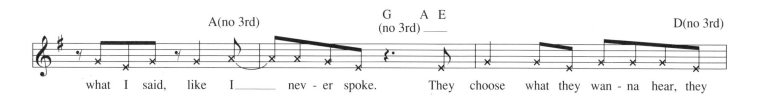

what I said, like I ____ nev - er spoke. They choose what they wan - na hear, they

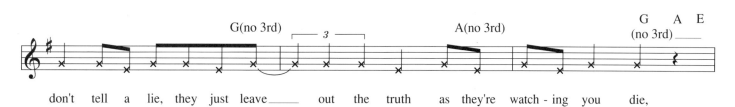

don't tell a lie, they just leave ____ out the truth as they're watch - ing you die,

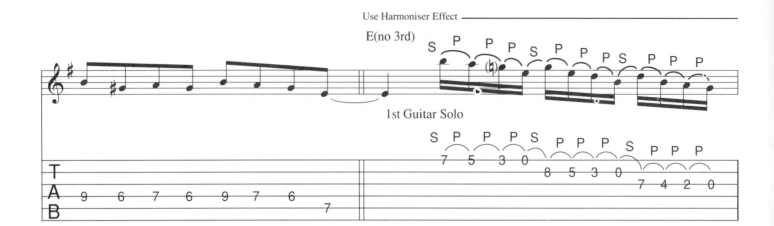

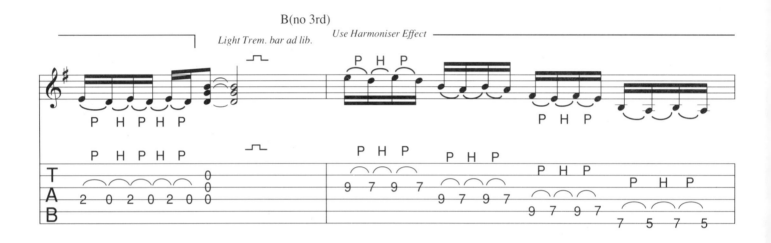

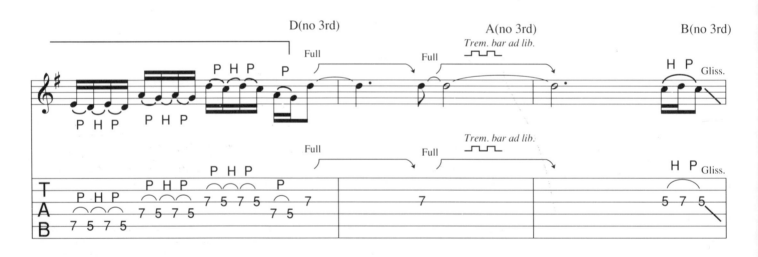

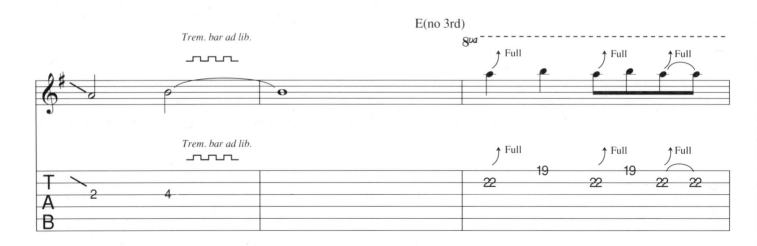

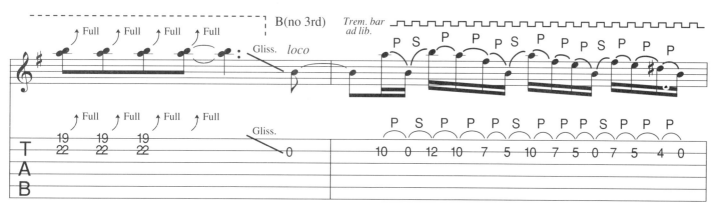

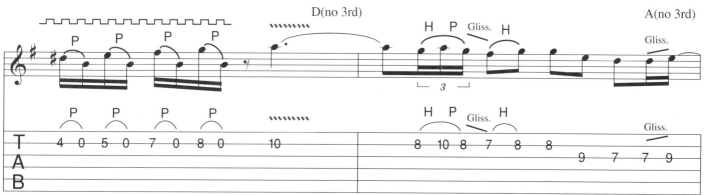

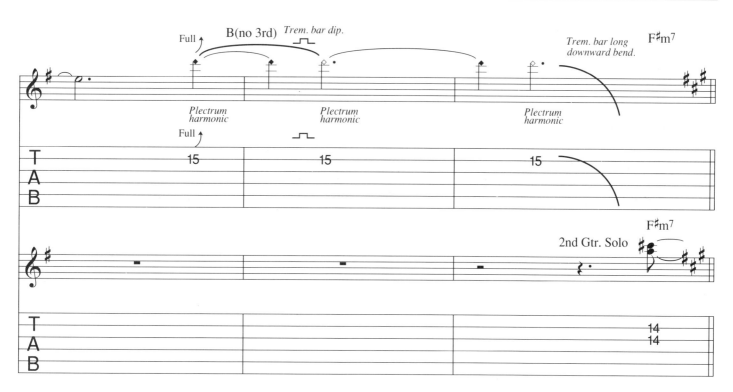

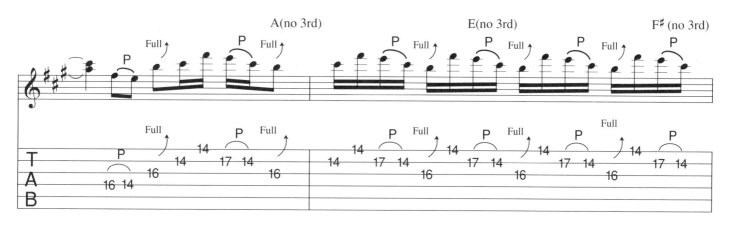

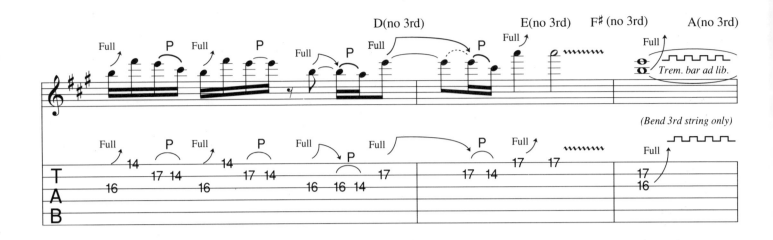

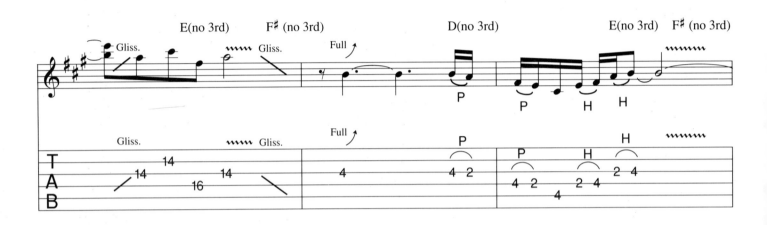

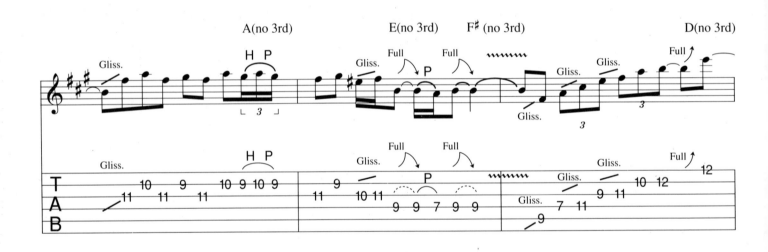

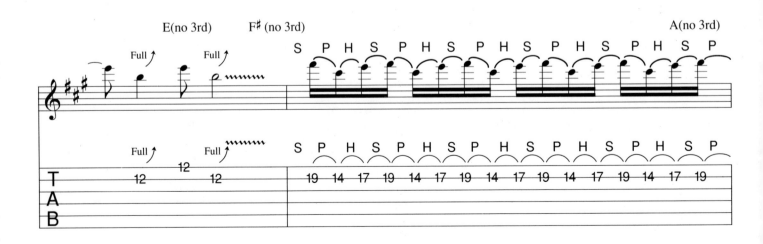

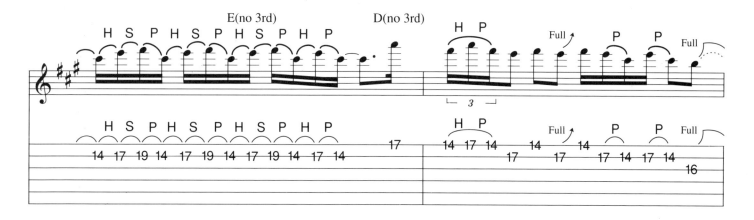

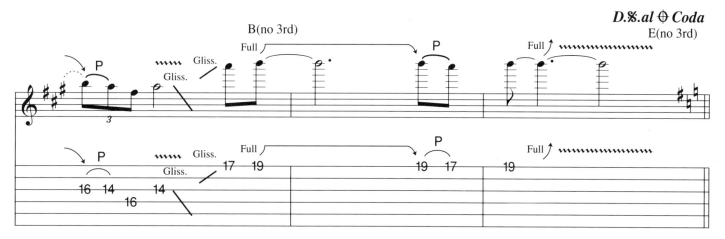

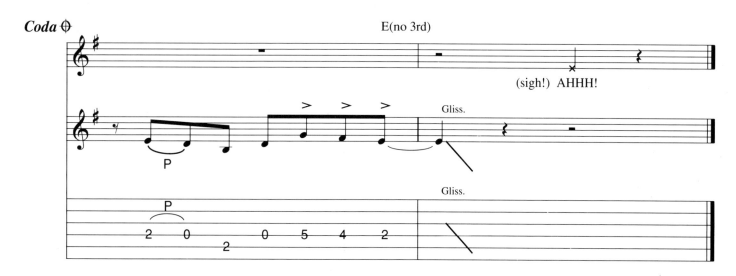

Verse 2:
Jimmy Reptile and all his friends
Say they gonna be with you at the end
Burning records burning books
Holy soldiers Nazi looks
Crocodile smiles just wait a while
Till the T.V. Queen gets her make up clean
I've lived in filfth I've lived in sin
And I still smell cleaner than the shit you're in

Verse 3:
They ain't religious but they ain't no fools
When Noah built his Cadillac it was cool
Two by two they're still going down
And the satellite circus just left town
I think they're strange and when they're dead
They can have a Lincoln for their bed
Friend of the President - trick of the tail
Now they ain't got a prayer - 100 years in jail

9/93(16062)

The Beatles

 Enya

 Phil Collins

 Van Morrison

 Bob Dylan

 Sting

 Paul Simon

 Tracy Chapman

 Eric Clapton

 Pink Floyd

 New Kids On The Block

 Bryan Adams

 Tina Turner

 Elton John

 Bee Gees

 Whitney Houston

AC/DC

Bringing you the words

All the latest in rock and pop. Plus the brightest and best in West End show scores. Music books for every instrument under the sun. And exciting new teach-yourself ideas like "Let's Play Keyboard" - in cassette/book packs, or on video. Available from all good music shops.

and music

Music Sales' complete catalogue lists thousands of titles and is available free from your local music shop, or direct from Music Sales Limited. Please send a cheque or postal order for £1.50 (for postage) to:

Music Sales Limited
Newmarket Road,
Bury St Edmunds,
Suffolk IP33 3YB

 Buddy

 Five Guys Named Moe

 Les Misérables

 West Side Story

 Phantom Of The Opera

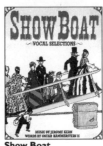 Show Boat

 The Rocky Horror Show

Bringing you the world's best music.

This superb folio celebrates all the great Iron Maiden singles of the last decade.
Twenty tracks arranged for guitar in tablature and standard notation.
Includes lyrics and guitar chord symbols.

2 MINUTES TO MIDNIGHT
ACES HIGH
BRING YOUR DAUGHTER...TO THE SLAUGHTER
CAN I PLAY WITH MADNESS?
FLIGHT OF ICARUS
HOLY SMOKE
INFINITE DREAMS
PURGATORY
RUN TO THE HILLS
RUNNING FREE

SANCTUARY
STRANGER IN A STRANGE LAND
THE CLAIRVOYANT
THE EVIL THAT MEN DO
THE NUMBER OF THE BEAST
THE TROOPER
TWILIGHT ZONE
WASTED YEARS
WOMEN IN UNIFORM
WRATHCHILD

ISBN 0-7119-2577-1

9 780711 925779

WISE PUBLICATIONS
Order No. AM84054

30plus

Trios For Flutes

arranged by
John Cacavas